QUIETING
Your Heart

FOR THE HOLIDAYS

30-DAY
PRAYER
JOURNAL

DARLENE
SCHACHT

All Scripture is taken from The KJV Bible

Quieting Your Heart for the Holidays: 30-Day Prayer Journal

Time-Warp Wife
Suite 5-1377 Border Street
Winnipeg, Manitoba
R3H ON1

ISBN 978-0-9780262-6-4

Find Darlene Schacht on the web here:
Blog: TimeWarpWife.com
Facebook: timewarpwife
Twitter: timewarpwife
Pinterest: timewarpwife

The Christmas Story

LUKE 2:1-20

And it came to pass in those days, that there went out a decree from Caesar Augustus that all the world should be taxed. (And this taxing was first made when Cyrenius was governor of Syria.)

And all went to be taxed, every one into his own city. And Joseph also went up from Galilee, out of the city of Nazareth, into Judaea, unto the city of David, which is called Bethlehem; (because he was of the house and lineage of David:) To be taxed with Mary his espoused wife, being great with child.

And so it was, that, while they were there, the days were accomplished that she should be delivered. And she brought forth her firstborn son, and wrapped him in swaddling clothes, and laid him in a manger; because there was no room for them in the inn.

And there were in the same country shepherds abiding in the field, keeping watch over their flock by night. And, lo, the angel of the Lord came upon them, and the glory of the Lord shone round about them: and they were sore afraid.

And the angel said unto them, "Fear not: for, behold, I bring you good tidings of great joy, which shall be to all people.

For unto you is born this day in the city of David a Saviour, which is Christ the Lord. And this shall be a sign unto you; Ye shall find the babe wrapped in swaddling clothes, lying in a manger."

And suddenly there was with the angel a multitude of the heavenly host praising God, and saying, "Glory to God in the highest, and on earth peace, good will toward men."

And it came to pass, as the angels were gone away from them into heaven, the shepherds said one to another, Let us now go even unto Bethlehem, and see this thing which is come to pass, which the Lord hath made known unto us.

And they came with haste, and found Mary, and Joseph, and the babe lying in a manger. And when they had seen it, they made known abroad the saying which was told them concerning this child.

And all they that heard it wondered at those things which were told them by the shepherds. But Mary kept all these things, and pondered them in her heart.

And the shepherds returned, glorifying and praising God for all the things that they had heard and seen, as it was told unto them.

TODAY'S PRAYER

God is...

Glory to God in the highest, and on earth peace, good will toward men.
Luke 2:14

3 THINGS I'M THANKFUL FOR

PEACE

DAY 1

Memories

record a little snapshot
of your day

_____

_____
_____
_____
_____
_____
_____

Start a diarized list of everything you need to get done this holiday season. I've provided space at the back of this journal, so you can look back on your to-do list year after year.

This Christmas...

I want to... _____
_____
_____
_____

TODAY'S PRAYER

_____
_____
_____
_____
_____
_____
_____
_____
_____
_____
_____
_____
_____

3 THINGS I'M THANKFUL FOR

For God so loved the world, that he gave his only begotten Son, that whosoever believeth in him should not perish, but have everlasting life.

John 3:16

DAY 2

Memories

record a little
snapshot of today

_____

_____
_____
_____
_____
_____

Light a large Christmas candle during the holiday
season as a symbol of God's faithfulness. Slip prayer
requests under the candle every now and then.
Pray together each night before blowing it out.

This Christmas...

I want to... _____
_____
_____
_____

TODAY'S PRAYER

Now the God of hope fill you with all joy and peace in believing, that ye may abound in hope, through the power of the Holy Ghost.

Romans 15:13

3 THINGS I'M THANKFUL FOR

DAY 3

Memories

record a little
snapshot of today

_____
_____
_____
_____
_____
_____

There's more to Advent than calendars.
You might enjoy daily Advent devotions that
point your family to Christ.

This Christmas...

I want to... _____
_____
_____
_____

TODAY'S PRAYER

God is...

3 THINGS I'M THANKFUL FOR

Thanks be unto God for His unspeakable gift.
2 Corinthians 9:15

DAY 4

Memories

record a little
snapshot of today

_____

_____
_____
_____
_____
_____
_____

Psst... Christmas cards should be mailed out
during the first week of December so they
arrive mid month.

This Christmas...

I want to... _____
_____
_____
_____

As for me and my house, we will serve the Lord.

Joshua 24:15

3 THINGS I'M THANKFUL FOR

DAY 5

Memories

record a little snapshot
of your day

_____

_____
_____
_____
_____
_____
_____

Create a bucket list this holiday season.
Combine some old family traditions
with a few ideas that are brand-spanking
new to your family.

This Christmas...

I want to..._____
_____
_____
_____

TODAY'S PRAYER

_____
_____
_____
_____
_____
_____
_____
_____
_____
_____
_____
_____
_____

Let the peace of God rule in your hearts, to the which also ye are called in one body; and be ye thankful.

Colossians 3:15

3 THINGS I'M THANKFUL FOR

Christmas List

DAY 6

Memories

record a little
snapshot of today

_____

_____
_____
_____
_____
_____
_____

*Plan a few blessing bombs throughout the holiday
season. Choose a few families that you want to bless,
then decide on unique ways to bring them joy.*

This Christmas...

I want to...
_____
_____
_____
_____

_____

_____

_____

_____

_____

_____

_____

_____

_____

_____

_____

3 THINGS I'M THANKFUL FOR

Looking unto Jesus the author and finisher of our faith; who for the joy that was set before him endured the cross, despising the shame, and is set down at the right hand of the throne of God.

Hebrews 12:2

DAY 7

Memories

record a little snapshot
of your day

_____

_____
_____
_____
_____
_____
_____

Instead of exchanging gifts, some families exchange letters telling each other how much that person means to them. What a beautiful idea!

This Christmas...

I want to...
_____
_____
_____
_____

TODAY'S PRAYER

_____
_____
_____
_____
_____
_____
_____
_____
_____
_____
_____
_____
_____

3 THINGS I'M THANKFUL FOR

Rejoice greatly, O daughter of Zion; shout, O daughter of Jerusalem: behold, thy King cometh unto thee.

Zechariah 9:9

DAY 8

Memories

record a little
snapshot of today

_____

_____
_____
_____
_____
_____
_____

Soft music brings warmth and joy to a home.
Create a seasonal playlist, and use it
as background music.

This Christmas...

I want to... _____
_____
_____
_____

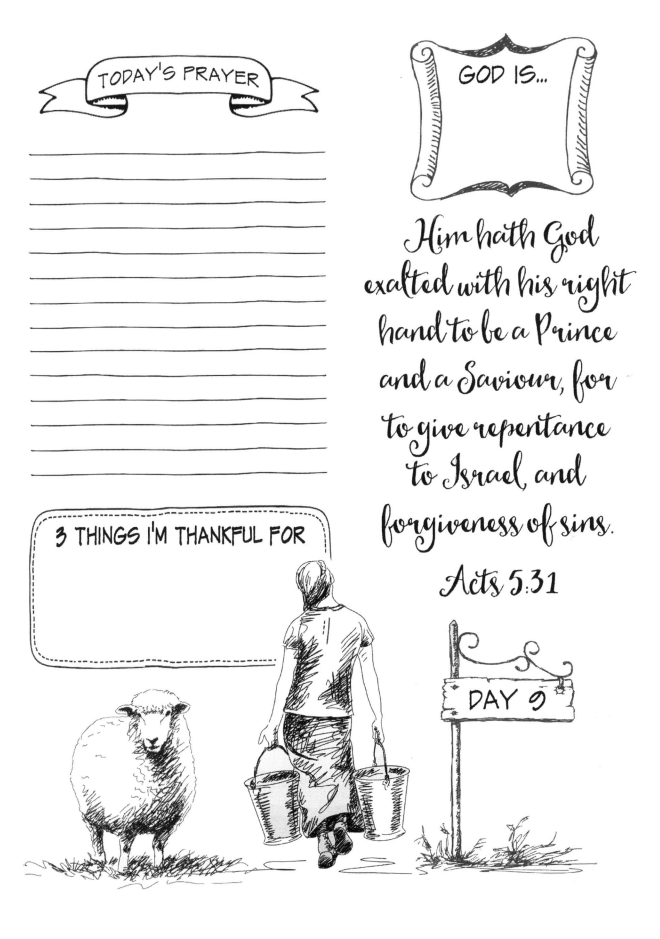

TODAY'S PRAYER

GOD IS...

3 THINGS I'M THANKFUL FOR

Him hath God exalted with his right hand to be a Prince and a Saviour, for to give repentance to Israel, and forgiveness of sins.

Acts 5:31

DAY 9

Memories

record a little snapshot
of your day

_____
_____
_____
_____
_____
_____

Pick up some scented candles like cinnamon and
apple pie. The smell will make your
house feel like home.

This Christmas...

I want to..._____
_____
_____
_____

TODAY'S PRAYER

And the angel said unto them, Fear not: for, behold, I bring you good tidings of great joy, which shall be to all people.

Luke 2:10

3 THINGS I'M THANKFUL FOR

DAY 10

Memories

record a little snapshot of your day

_____

_____

_____

_____

_____

_____

_____

Focus on organizing one area of your home every day, like a closet, a cupboard, or drawer...
This will make holiday cleanup easier!

This Christmas...

I want to... _____

_____

_____

_____

TODAY'S PRAYER

3 THINGS I'M THANKFUL FOR

And this shall be a sign unto you; Ye shall find the babe wrapped in swaddling clothes, lying in a manger.

Luke 2:12

DAY II

Memories

record a little
snapshot of today

_____

_____
_____
_____
_____
_____
_____

Is the holiday season more stressful than you'd
like it to be? Try down-sizing. Ask yourself what you
should keep, and what you can cut.

This Christmas...

I want to..._____
_____
_____
_____

For unto us a child is born, unto us a son is given: and the government shall be upon his shoulder: and his name shall be called Wonderful, Counsellor, The mighty God, The everlasting Father, The Prince of Peace.

Isaiah 9:6

3 THINGS I'M THANKFUL FOR

DAY 12

Memories

record a little
snapshot of today

_____

_____
_____
_____
_____
_____
_____

The Bible says, "A merry heart doeth good like medicine." Keep this in mind when you're giving and serving this holiday season. Do nothing merely for the sake of duty, but rather with gladness and joy.

This Christmas...

I want to... _____
_____
_____
_____

TODAY'S PRAYER

_____
_____
_____
_____
_____
_____
_____
_____
_____
_____
_____
_____
_____
_____

3 THINGS I'M THANKFUL FOR

GOD IS...

Now faith is the substance of things hoped for, the evidence of things not seen.

Hebrews 11:1

DAY 13

Memories

record a little
snapshot of today

_____

_____
_____
_____
_____
_____
_____

Find recipes you can make ahead of time
and freeze them. Start early so you can relax
a little as Christmas approaches.

This Christmas...

I want to... _____
_____
_____
_____

TODAY'S PRAYER

_____
_____
_____
_____
_____
_____
_____
_____
_____
_____
_____
_____
_____
_____

3 THINGS I'M THANKFUL FOR

Behold, a virgin shall be with child, and shall bring forth a son, and they shall call his name Emmanuel, which being interpreted is, God with us.

Matthew 1:23

DAY 14

Memories

record a little
snapshot of today

_____

_____
_____
_____
_____
_____
_____

Don't stretch your budget thin. Simplify.
There are countless ways to bless
without financial stress.

This Christmas...

I want to... _____
_____
_____
_____

TODAY'S PRAYER

_____
_____
_____
_____
_____
_____
_____
_____
_____
_____
_____
_____
_____

Every good gift and every perfect gift is from above, and cometh down from the Father of lights, with whom is no variableness, neither shadow of turning.

James 1:17

3 THINGS I'M THANKFUL FOR

DAY 15

Memories

record a little snapshot
of your day

_____

_____
_____
_____
_____
_____
_____

Focus on one little corner of your home today.
Put in the effort to make it pretty,
comfy, inviting, and warm.

This Christmas...

I want to... _____
_____
_____
_____

TODAY'S PRAYER

_____
_____
_____
_____
_____
_____
_____
_____
_____
_____
_____
_____
_____
_____
_____

3 THINGS I'M THANKFUL FOR

Now the God of hope fill you with all joy and peace in believing, that ye may abound in hope, through the power of the Holy Ghost.

Romans 15:13

PEACE

DAY 16

Memories

record a little
snapshot of today

_____

_____
_____
_____
_____
_____
_____

Taking on too much, expecting too much, or putting pressure on yourself can be a distraction. He's the reason for the season. Don't lose sight of that.

This Christmas...

I want to...
_____
_____
_____
_____

God Is...

Let us hold fast the profession of our faith without wavering; (for he is faithful that promised;)

Hebrews 10:23

3 PEOPLE TO PRAY FOR

DAY 17

Memories

record a little snapshot
of your day

_____
_____
_____
_____
_____

Don't have the time or money to decorate
your home for the holidays? Choose a focal
point. Place a few inexpensive items there, like
Christmas books, wrapped boxes, & candles.

This Christmas...

I want to... _____
_____
_____
_____

_____
_____
_____
_____
_____
_____
_____
_____
_____
_____
_____
_____
_____

3 THINGS I'M THANKFUL FOR

Peace I leave with you, my peace I give unto you: not as the world giveth, give I unto you. Let not your heart be troubled, neither let it be afraid.

John 14:27

DAY 18

Memories

record a little snapshot
of your day

_____

_____
_____
_____
_____
_____
_____

The best present one can give is their presence.
Make time for your loved ones this
Chirstmas. You'll be every bit
as blessed as they will.

This Christmas...

I want to... _____
_____
_____
_____

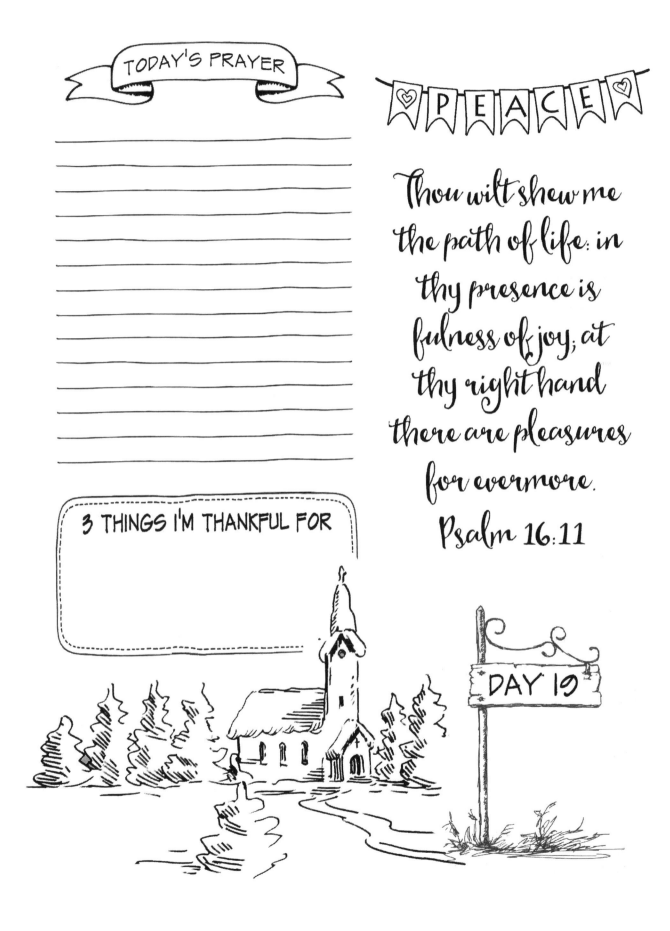

TODAY'S PRAYER

PEACE

Thou wilt shew me the path of life: in thy presence is fulness of joy; at thy right hand there are pleasures for evermore.

Psalm 16:11

3 THINGS I'M THANKFUL FOR

DAY 19

Memories

record a little
snapshot of today

_____

_____
_____
_____
_____
_____
_____

Don't put off for tomorrow what you can do today.
Start making your grocery list now,
if you haven't already.

This Christmas...

I want to..._____
_____
_____
_____

TODAY'S PRAYER

_____
_____
_____
_____
_____
_____
_____
_____
_____
_____
_____
_____

Greater love hath no man than this, that a man lay down his life for his friends.

John 15:13

3 THINGS I'M THANKFUL FOR

DAY 20

Memories

record a little snapshot
of your day

_____

_____

_____

_____

_____

_____

Put one night aside to look at Christmas lights.
Ask around before you go so you can
map your trip out, and catch the best displays.

This Christmas...

I want to..._____

_____

_____

_____

The grace of the Lord Jesus Christ, and the love of God, and the communion of the Holy Ghost, be with you all. Amen.

2 Corinthians 13:14

3 THINGS I'M THANKFUL FOR

Christmas List

DAY 21

Memories

record a little snapshot
of your day

_____

_____
_____
_____
_____
_____
_____

Tackle some of your Christmas to-dos with
a friend. Whether you're baking, filling
out cards, or wrapping gifts, enjoy these
moments together.

This Christmas...

I want to... _____
_____
_____
_____

_____
_____
_____
_____
_____
_____
_____
_____
_____
_____
_____

GOD IS...

Therefore being justified by faith, we have peace with God through our Lord Jesus Christ.

Romans 5:1

3 THINGS I'M THANKFUL FOR

DAY 22

Memories

record a little
snapshot of today

_____

_____
_____
_____
_____
_____
_____

Consider one thing (or two) that stresses
you out during the holiday season.
Decide in advance that you're choosing joy
this year, then tackle this task with smile.

This Christmas...

I want to... _____
_____
_____
_____

TODAY'S PRAYER

3 THINGS I'M THANKFUL FOR

And the peace of God, which passeth all understanding, shall keep your hearts and minds through Christ Jesus.

Philippians 4:7

DAY 23

Memories

record a little snapshot of your day

_____

_____
_____
_____
_____
_____
_____

Here's a gift idea...
Fill a few gift bags with goodies, hand
sanitizer, a comb, a toothbrush, chapstick, and
facial tissues. Deliver these bags to the homeless.

This Christmas...

I want to... _____
_____
_____
_____

TODAY'S PRAYER

_____
_____
_____
_____
_____
_____
_____
_____
_____
_____
_____
_____

GOD IS...

And they came with haste, and found Mary, and Joseph, and the babe lying in a manger.

Luke 2:16

3 THINGS I'M THANKFUL FOR

DAY 24

Memories

record a little
snapshot of today

_____

_____
_____
_____
_____
_____
_____

Give family members designated traditions that carry on year after year, such as making place settings, cutting down the tree, reading the Christmas story, or putting the star up.

This Christmas...

I want to... _____
_____
_____
_____

TODAY'S PRAYER

_____
_____
_____
_____
_____
_____
_____
_____
_____
_____
_____

3 THINGS I'M THANKFUL FOR

Rejoice in the Lord always: and again I say, Rejoice.
Philippians 4:4

DAY 25

Memories

record a little
snapshot of today

_____

_____

_____

_____

_____

_____

_____

Slow down and have some quiet time with the Lord.
After all, it's His birth we're celebrating, isn't it?

This Christmas...

I want to... _____

_____

_____

_____

TODAY'S PRAYER

3 THINGS I'M THANKFUL FOR

And the shepherds returned, glorifying and praising God for all the things that they had heard and seen, as it was told unto them.

Luke 2:20

DAY 26

Memories

record a little
snapshot of today

_____
_____
_____
_____
_____
_____

Make your home smell like the holidays!
Simmer a little vanilla, cinnamon, nutmeg,
and cloves in a pot on the stove.

This Christmas...

I want to..._____
_____
_____
_____

TODAY'S PRAYER

God is...

For the kingdom of God is not meat and drink; but righteousness, and peace, and joy in the Holy Ghost.
Romans 14:17

3 THINGS I'M THANKFUL FOR

DAY 27

Memories

record a little
snapshot of today

_____

_____
_____
_____
_____
_____
_____

Visit nativity scenes in your area. Leave a scented
candle along with a note, thanking them for
remembering Jesus this Christmas.

This Christmas...

I want to... _____
_____
_____
_____

TODAY'S PRAYER

GOD IS...

When they saw the star, they rejoiced with exceeding great joy.
Matthew 2:10

3 THINGS I'M THANKFUL FOR

DAY 28

Memories

record a little
snapshot of today

_____
_____
_____
_____
_____
_____

Place a pretty basket under the tree & fill it with things that you'll need Christmas morning like batteries, scissors, screwdrivers, and a trash bag.

This Christmas...

I want to...
_____
_____
_____
_____

TODAY'S PRAYER

_____
_____
_____
_____
_____
_____
_____
_____
_____
_____
_____
_____
_____

Therefore the Lord himself shall give you a sign; Behold, a virgin shall conceive, and bear a son, and shall call his name Immanuel..

Isaiah 7:14

3 THINGS I'M THANKFUL FOR

DAY 29

Memories

record a little
snapshot of today

_____

_____
_____
_____
_____
_____
_____

For many people, the holiday season is a difficult time. Pray for those who struggle with loneliness, and are suffering loss.

This Christmas...

I want to...
_____
_____
_____
_____

TODAY'S PRAYER

_____
_____
_____
_____
_____
_____
_____
_____
_____
_____
_____
_____
_____

For unto you is born this day in the city of David a Saviour, which is Christ the Lord.

Luke 2:11

3 THINGS I'M THANKFUL FOR

DAY 30

Memories

record a little
snapshot of today

_____

_____
_____
_____
_____
_____
_____

Don't look for perfection this Christmas. Don't focus
on what you don't have or where you fall short.
This isn't about you, your gifts, or your turkey...
It's about God's gift to the world through His son.

This Christmas...

I want to... _____
_____
_____
_____